It was that time of year when the night drew in around 4pm ...

AMBULANCE
SF12 JFG

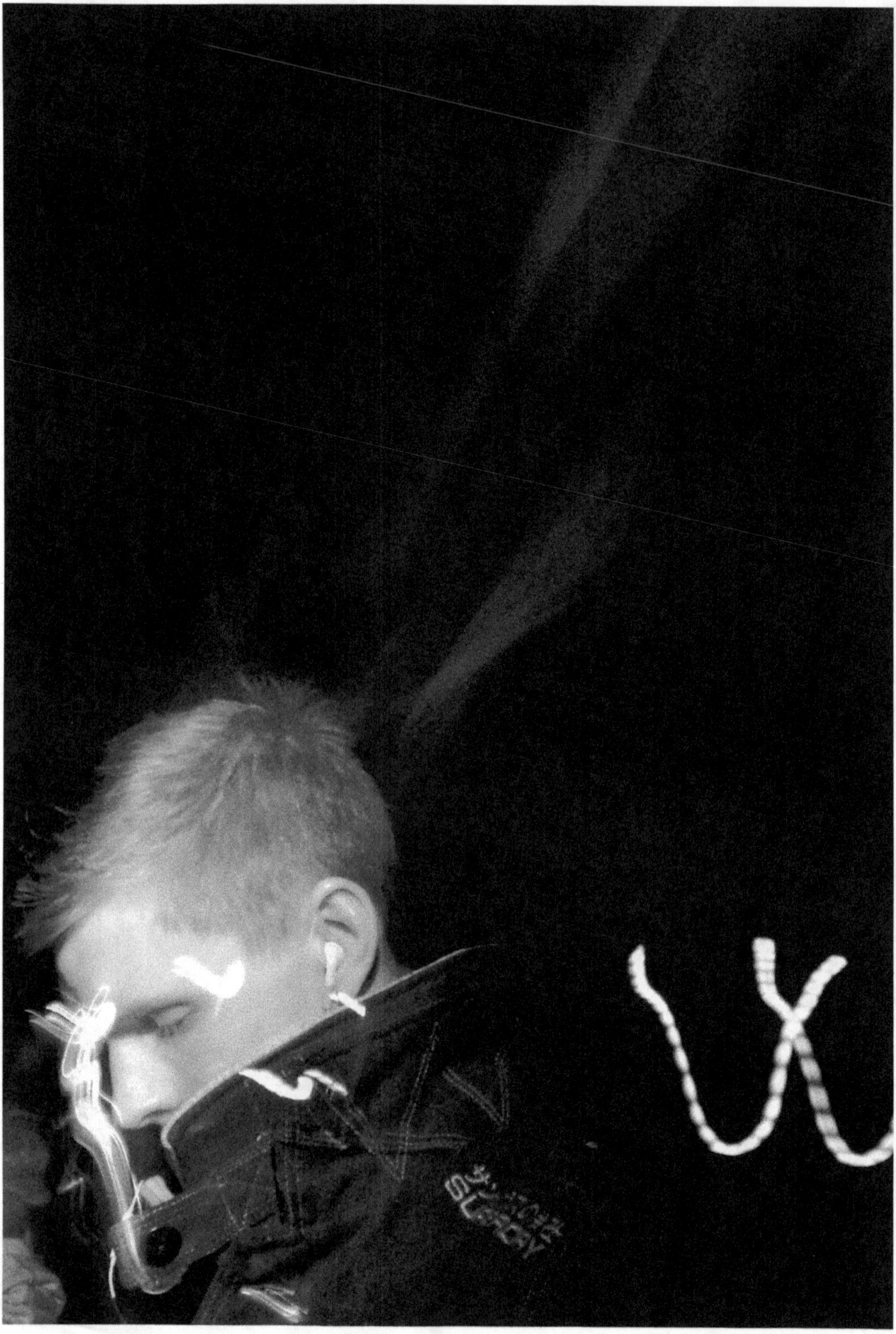

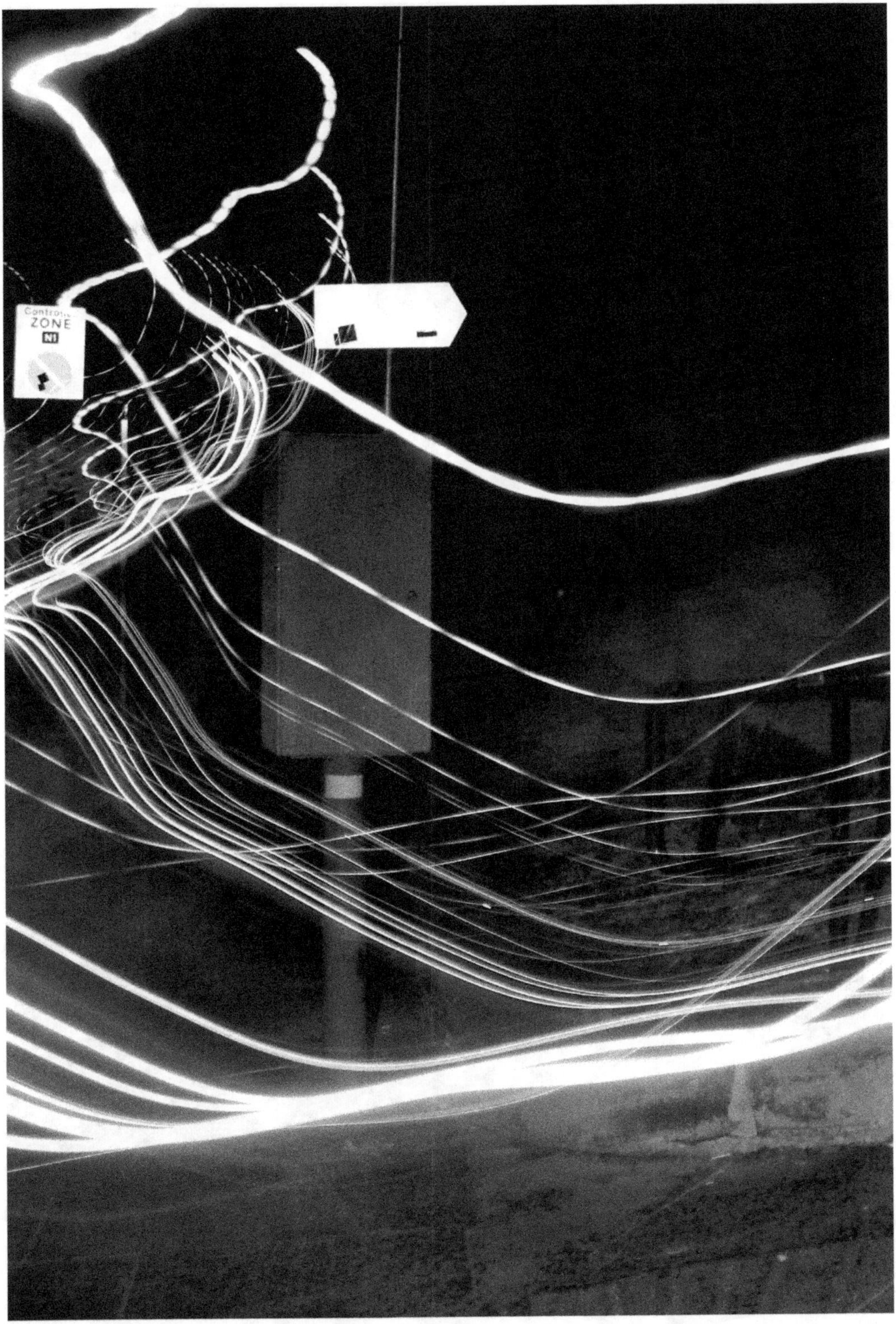
ZONE
NI

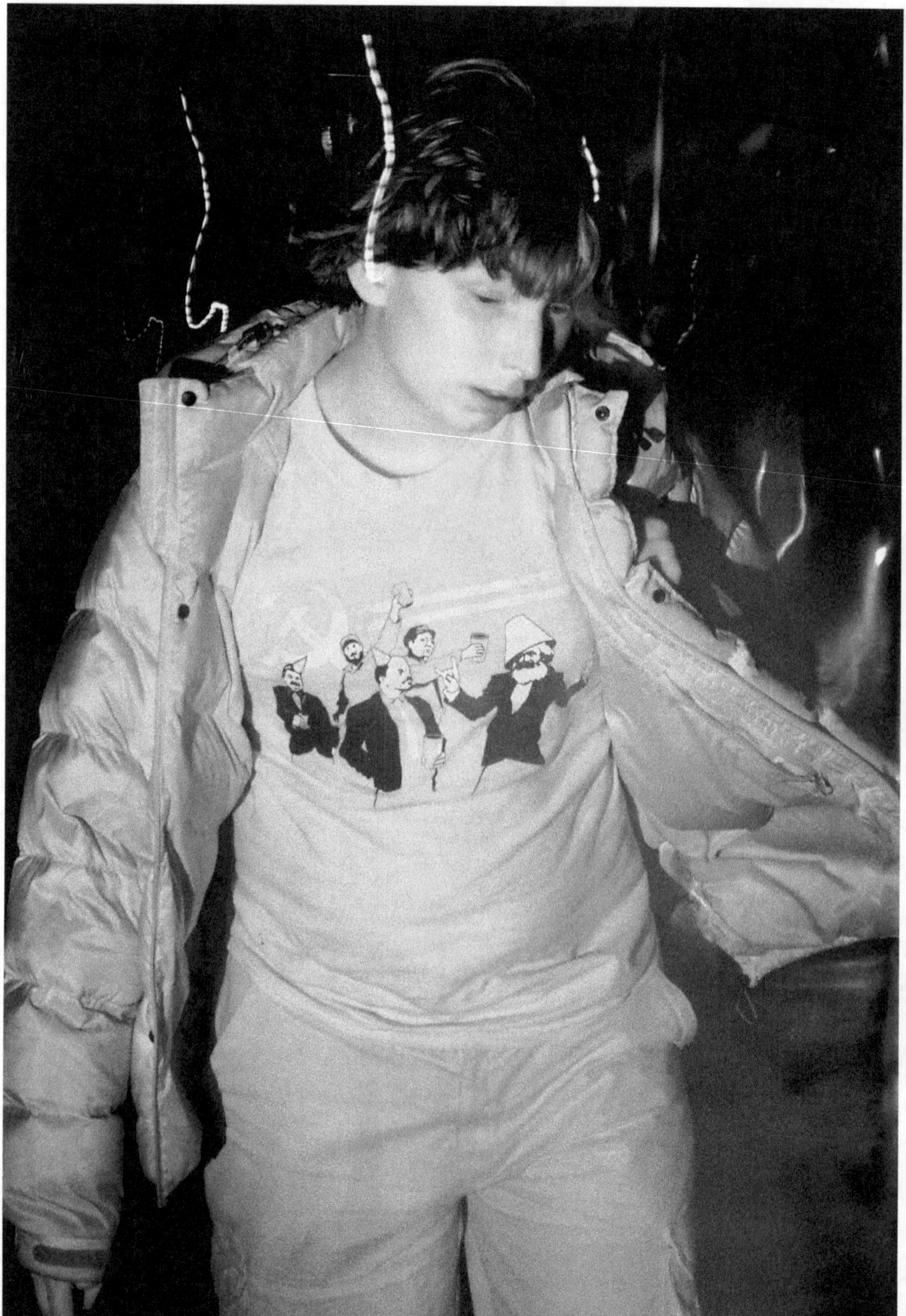

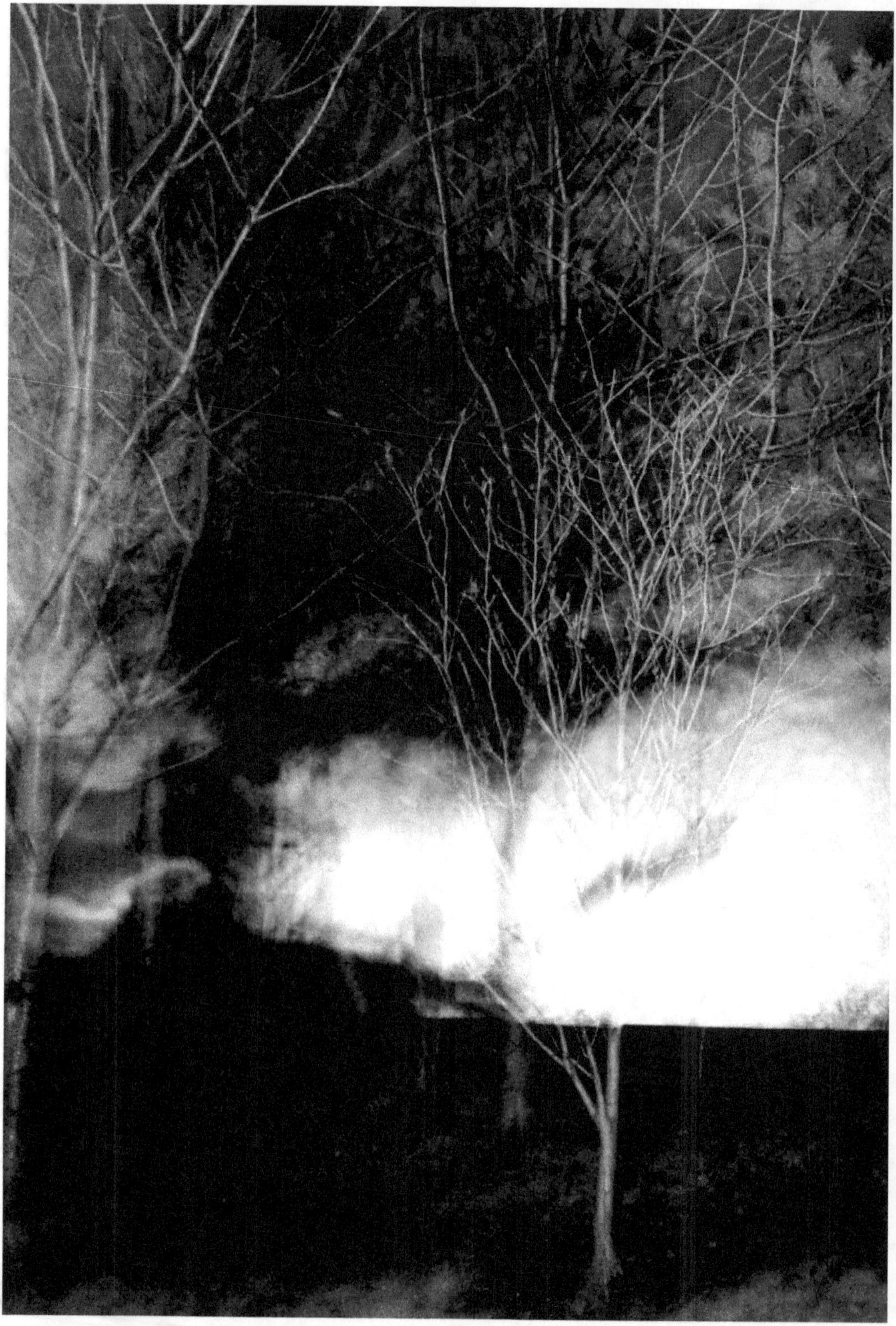

M
T
E
H
PARALETIC UNIVERSE

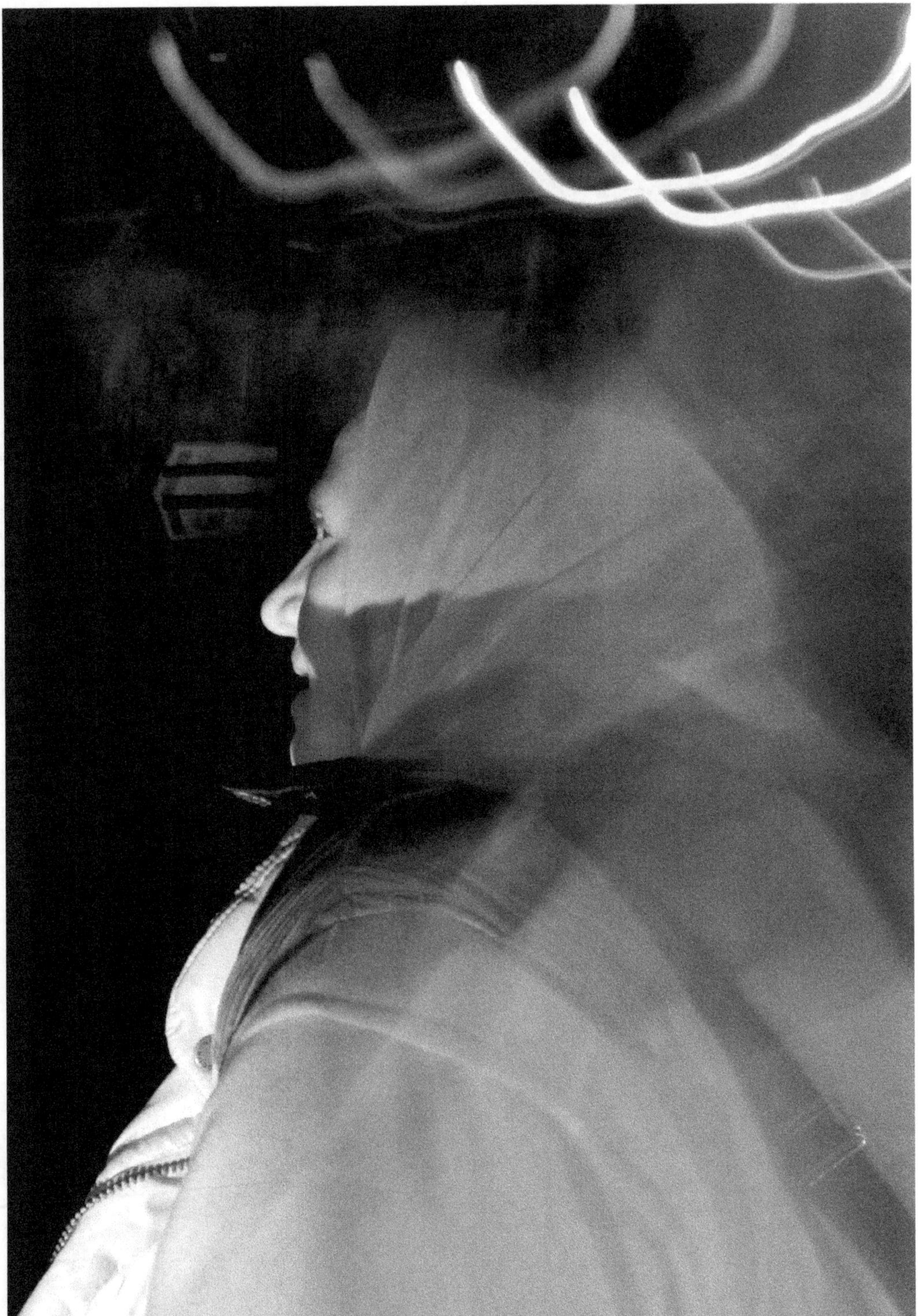

TOSHIBA

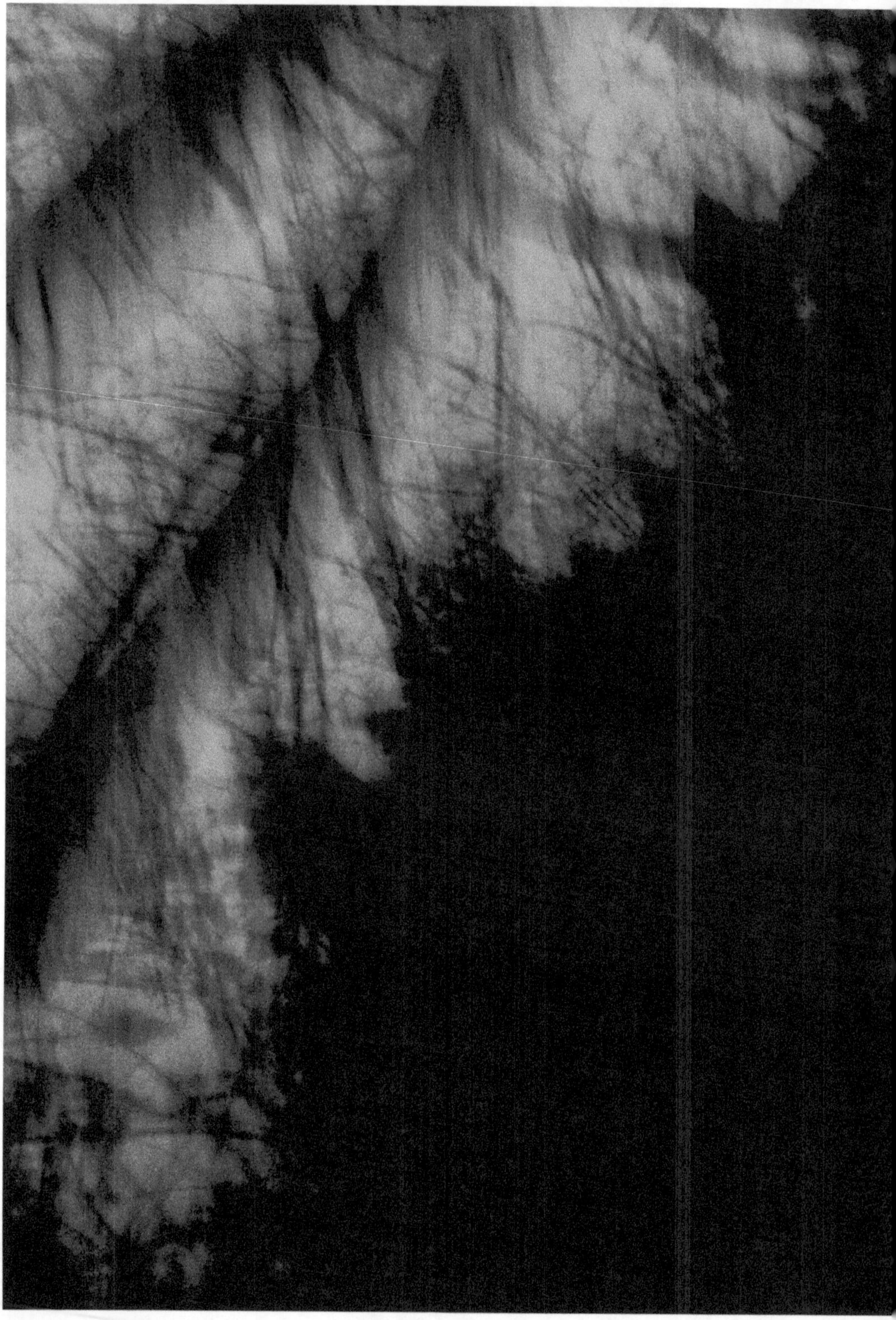

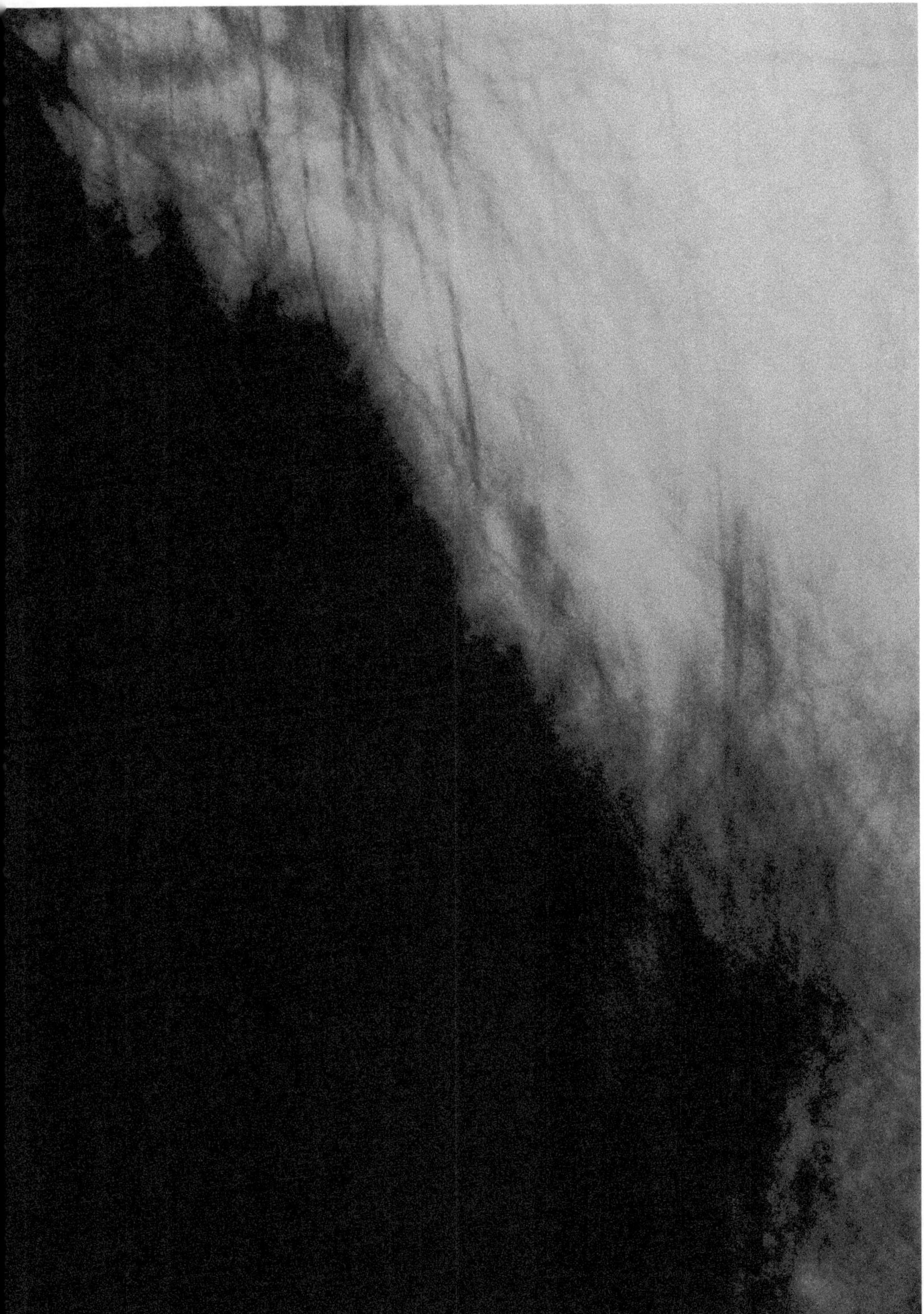

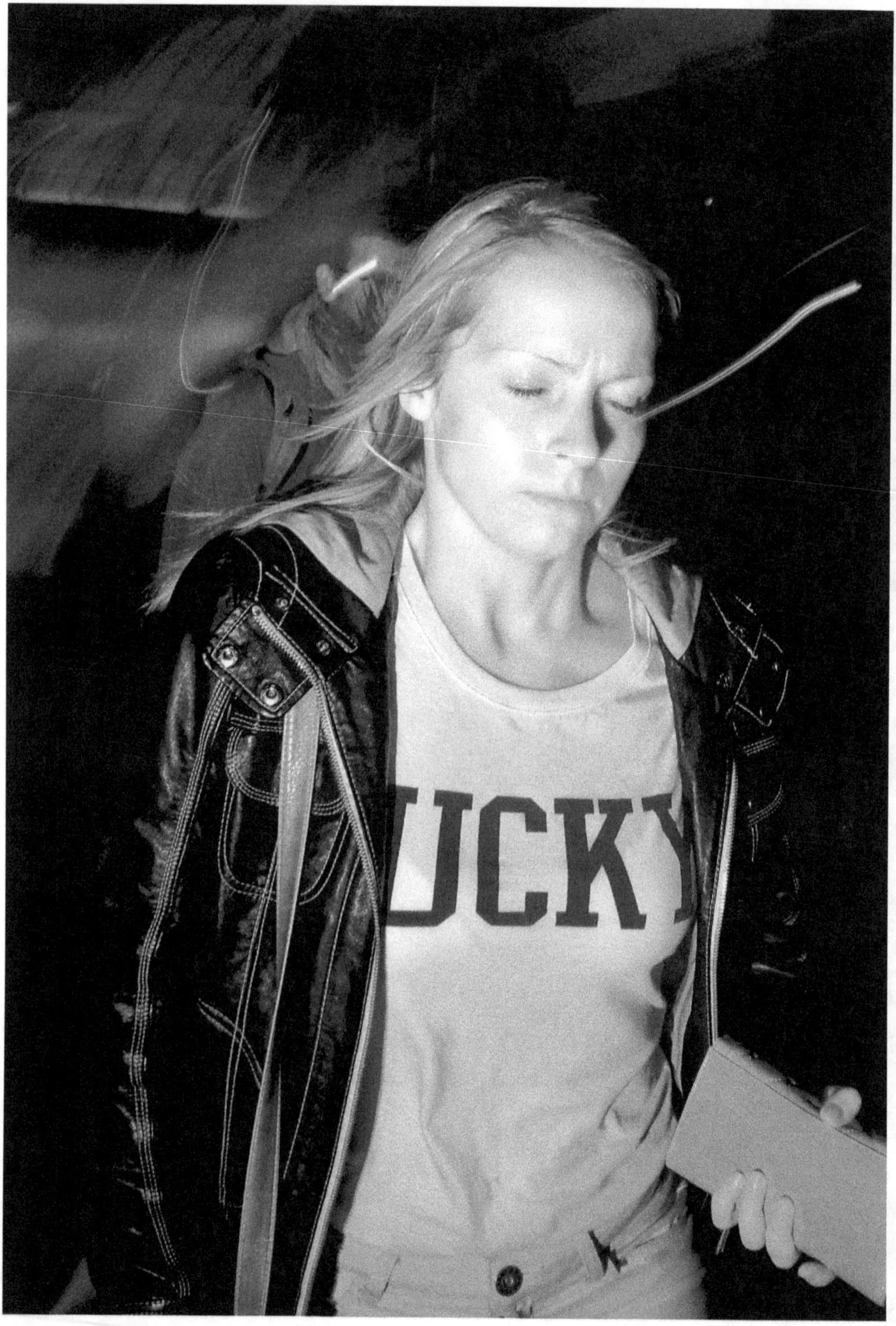
UCKY

GREENWAY
No stopping
Mon-Fri
7.30am-6.30pm
Sat
8.30am-6.30pm
All Other Routes
Leith

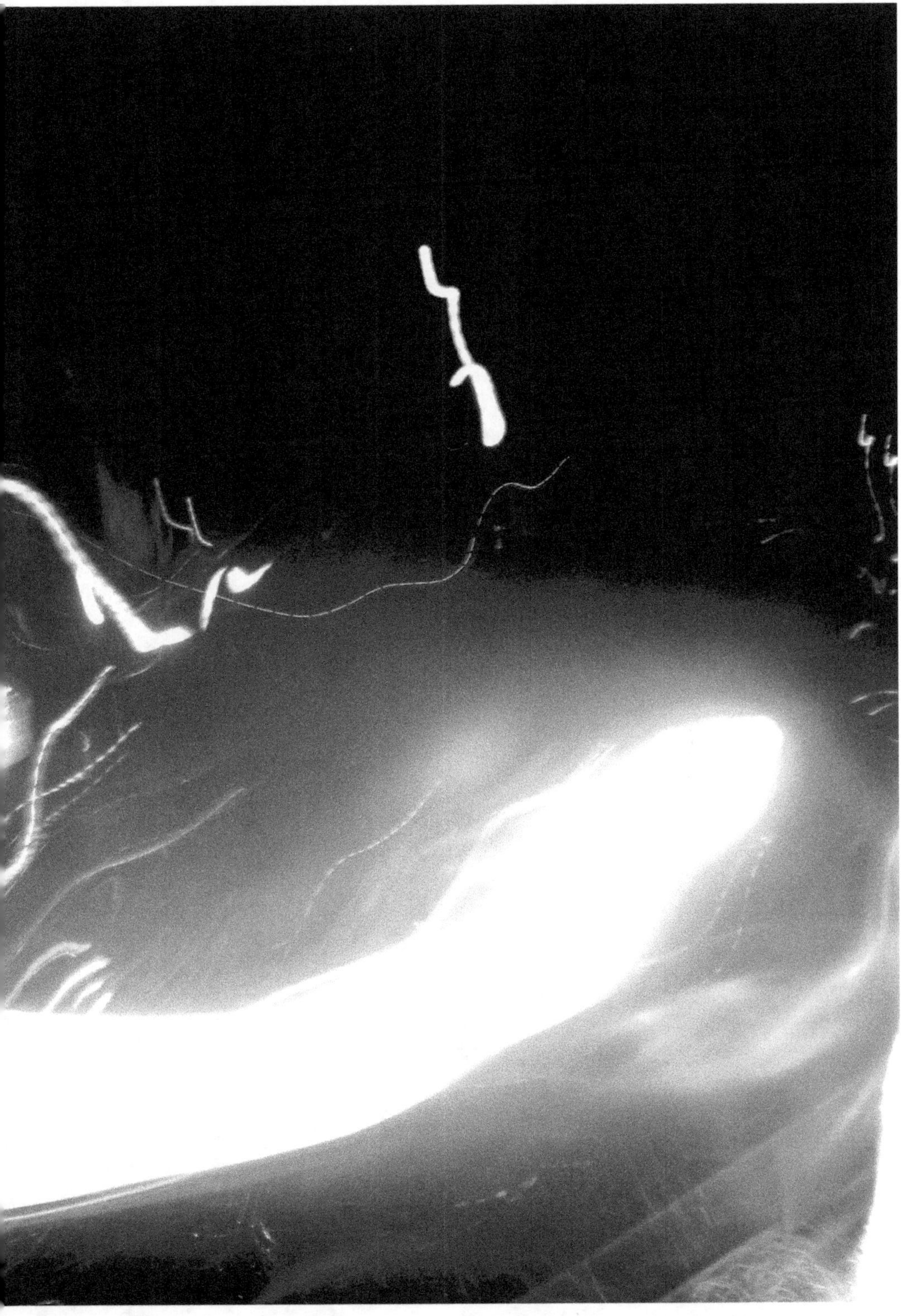

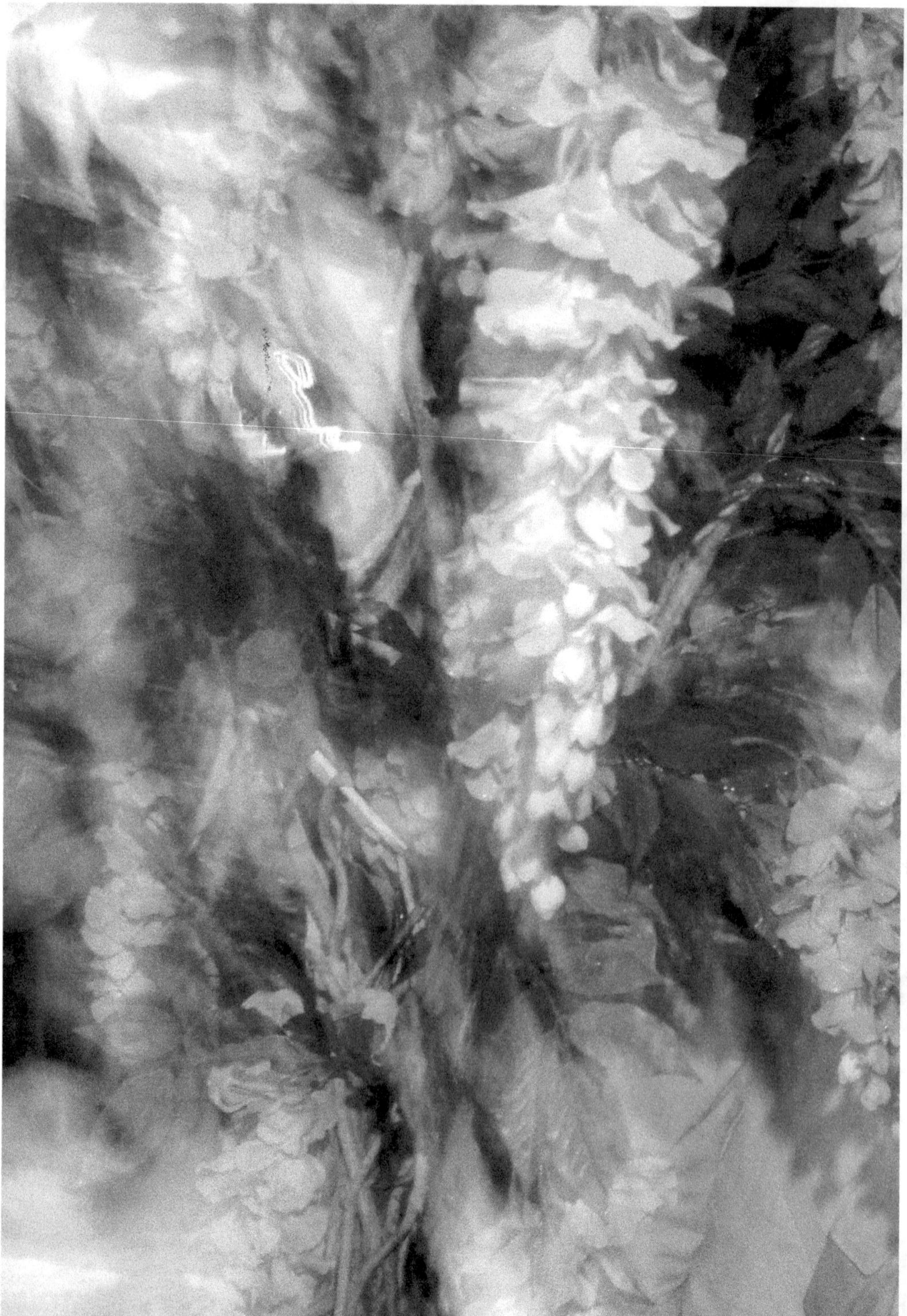

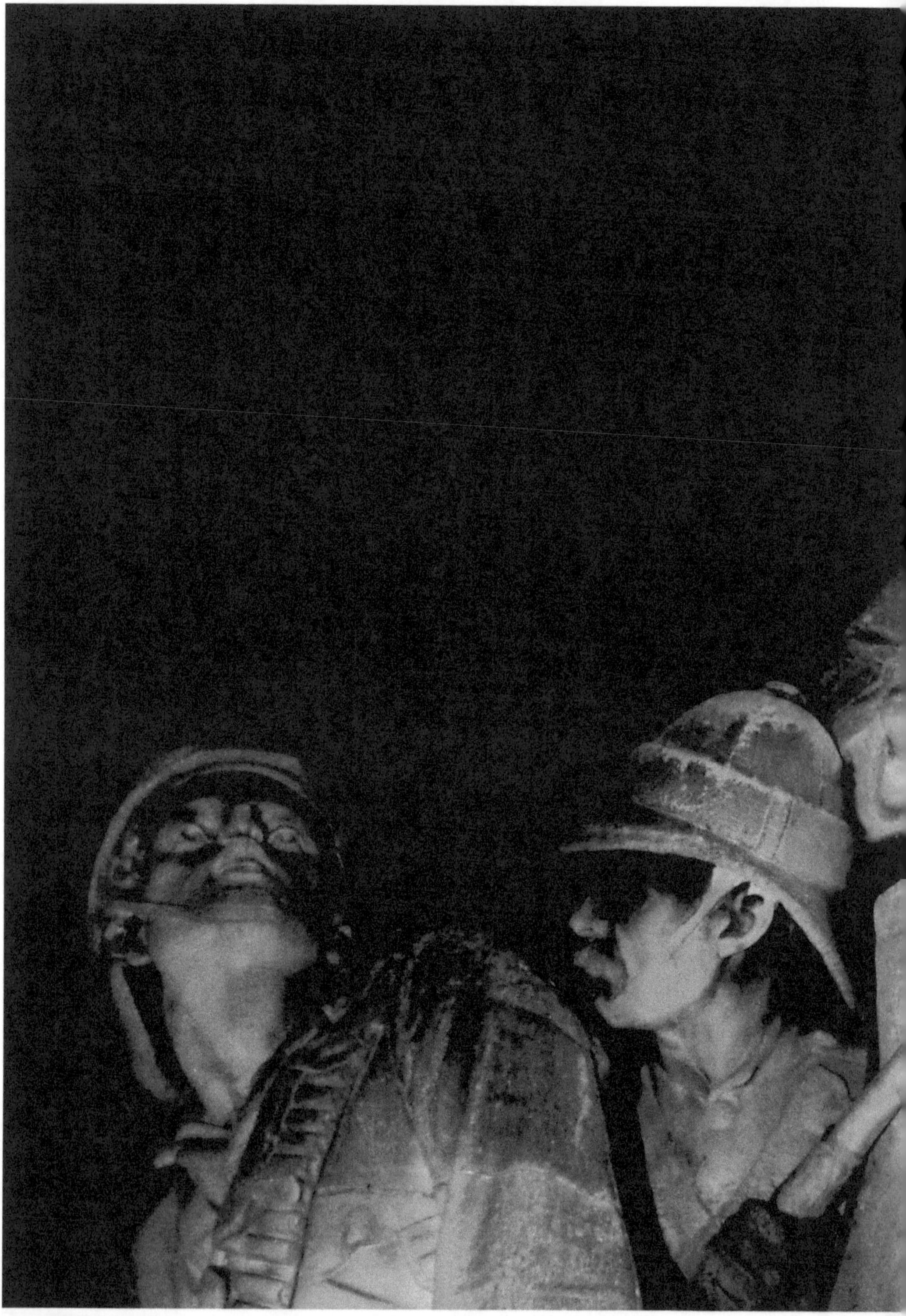

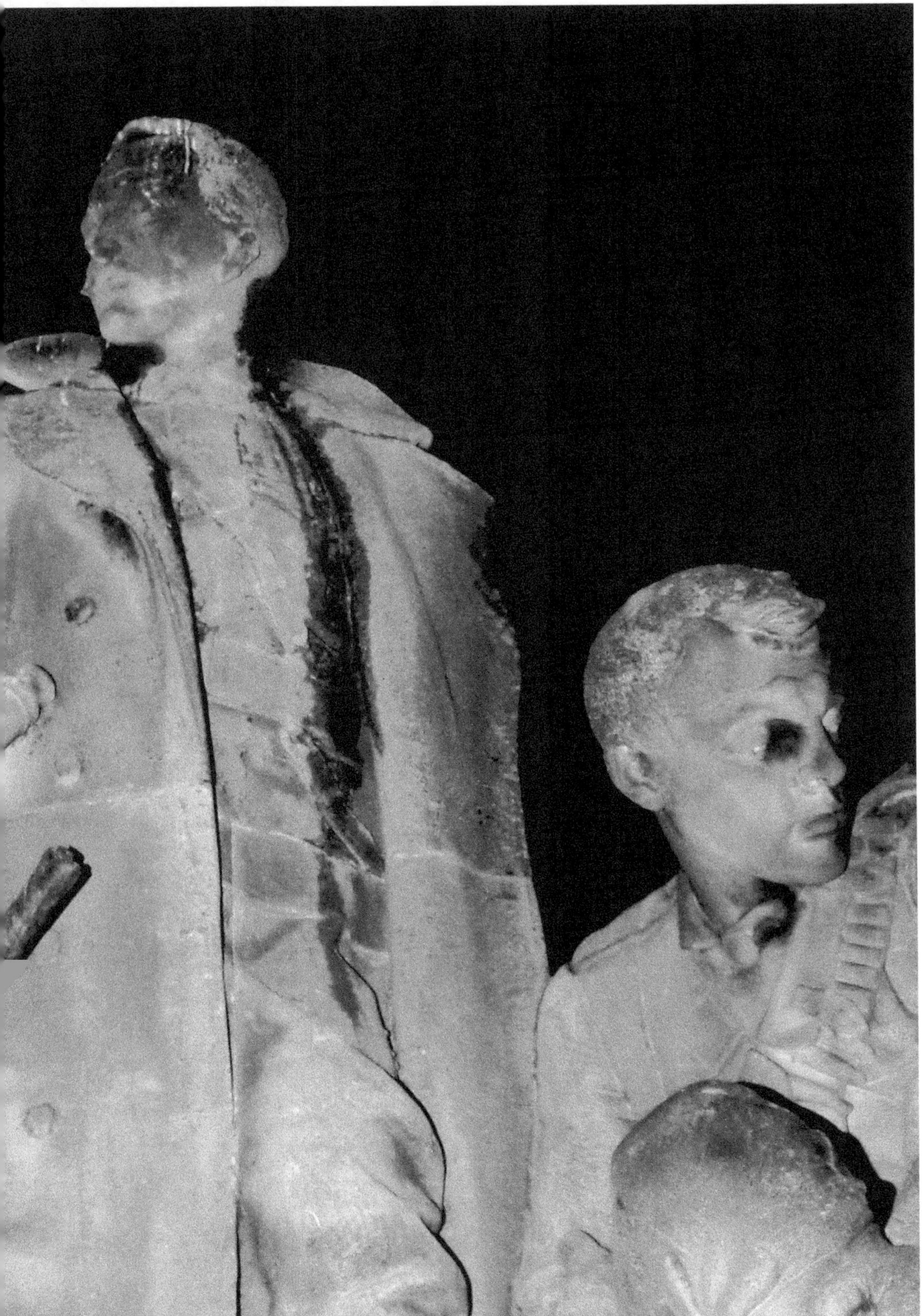

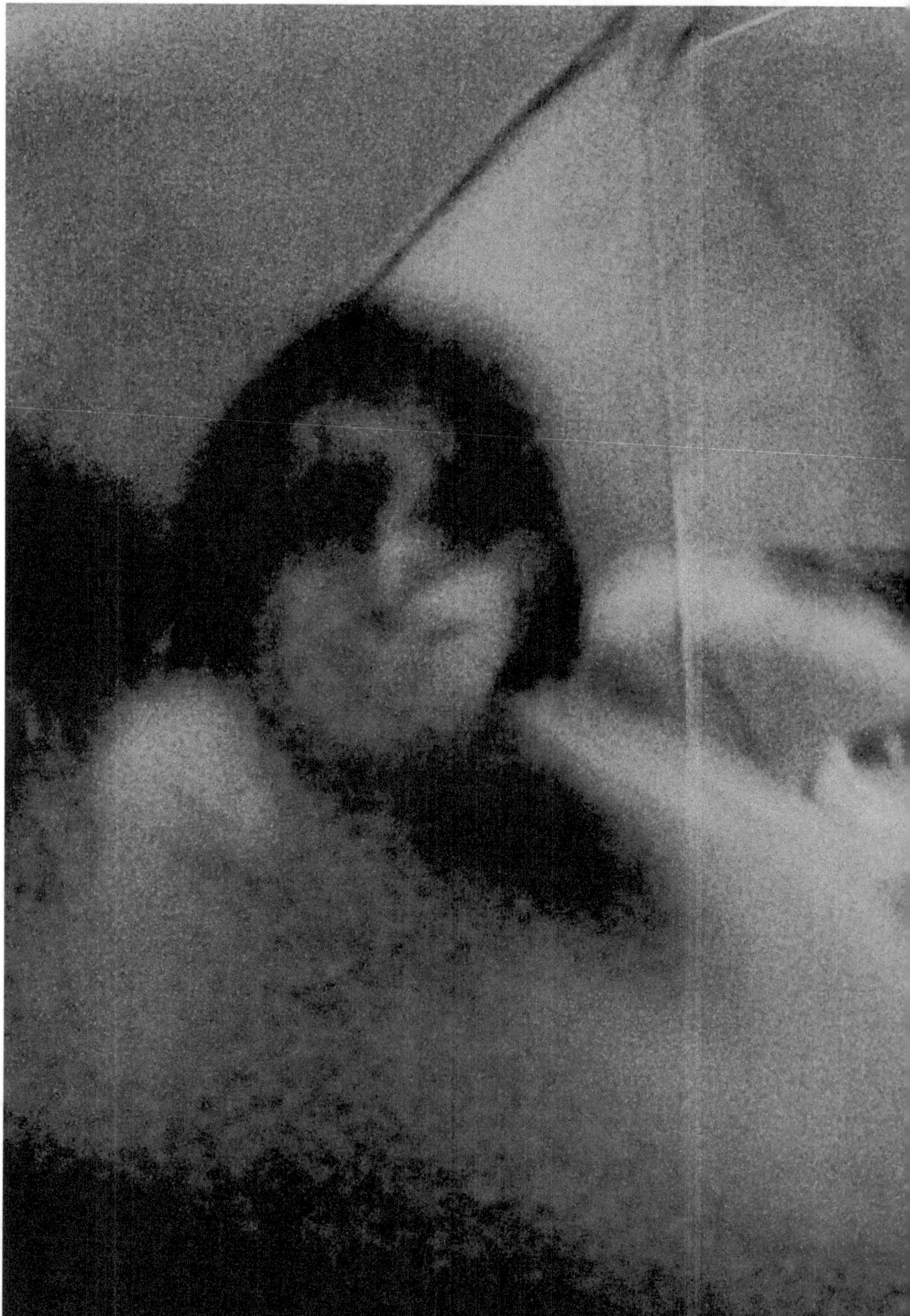

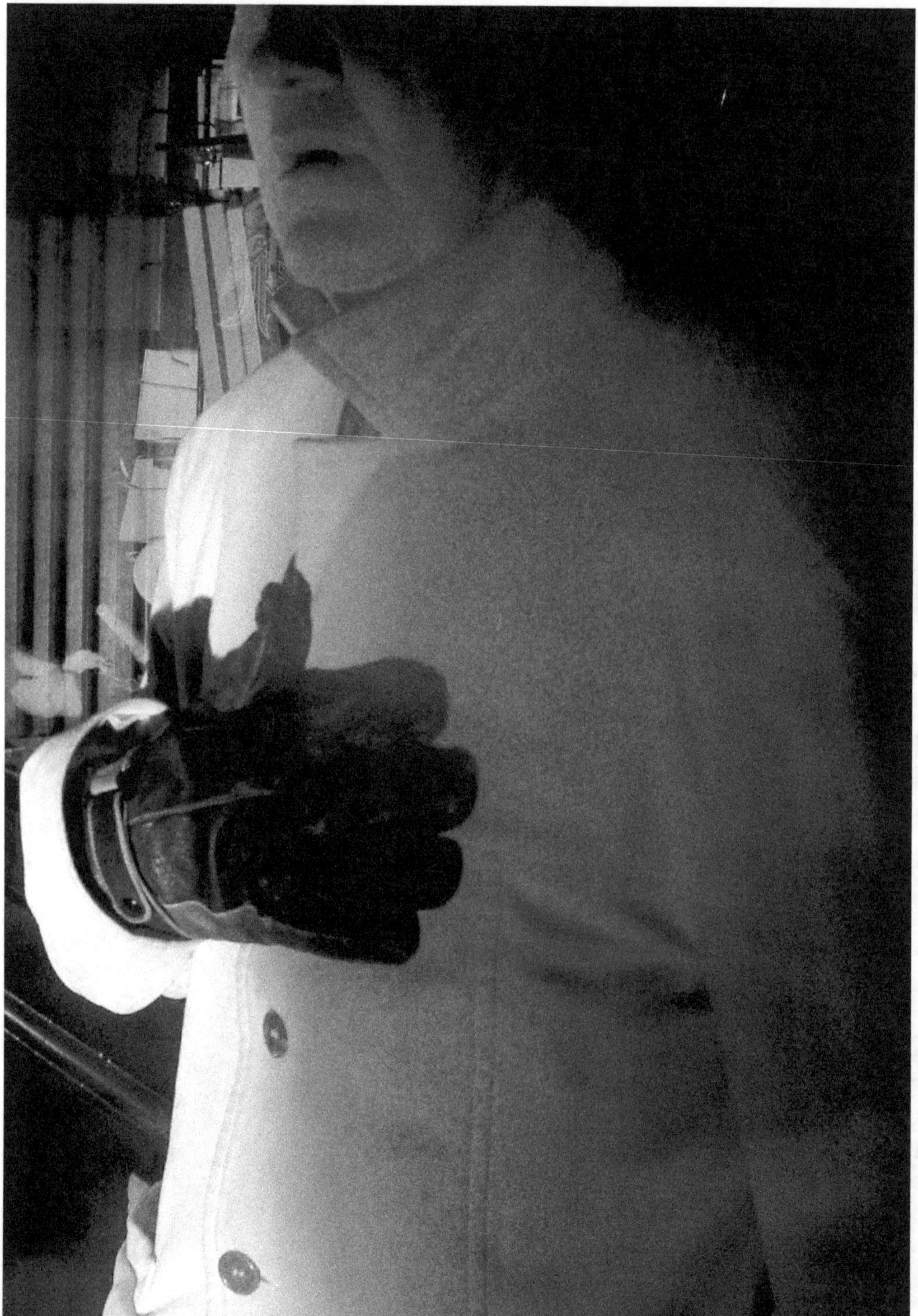

www.ingramcontent.com/pod-product-compliance
Lightning Source LLC
Chambersburg PA
CBHW072256170526
45158CB00003BA/1086
* 9 7 8 1 3 2 6 2 8 3 9 0 2 *